# 1001
# Animals to Spot

Ruth Brocklehurst

Illustrated by Teri Gower

Designed by Susannah Owen

Edited by Anna Milbourne

Natural history consultant: Dr. Margaret Rostron

For every book sold, the illustrator will make a donation to
Care for the Wild International.

# Contents

# Animals to spot

The pictures in this book show animals living all around the world. In each picture there are animals for you to find and count.

There are 1001 animals to spot altogether. The example pages below show what you need to do to find them.

Each little picture shows you what to look for in the big picture.

The blue number tells you how many of that animal you need to spot.

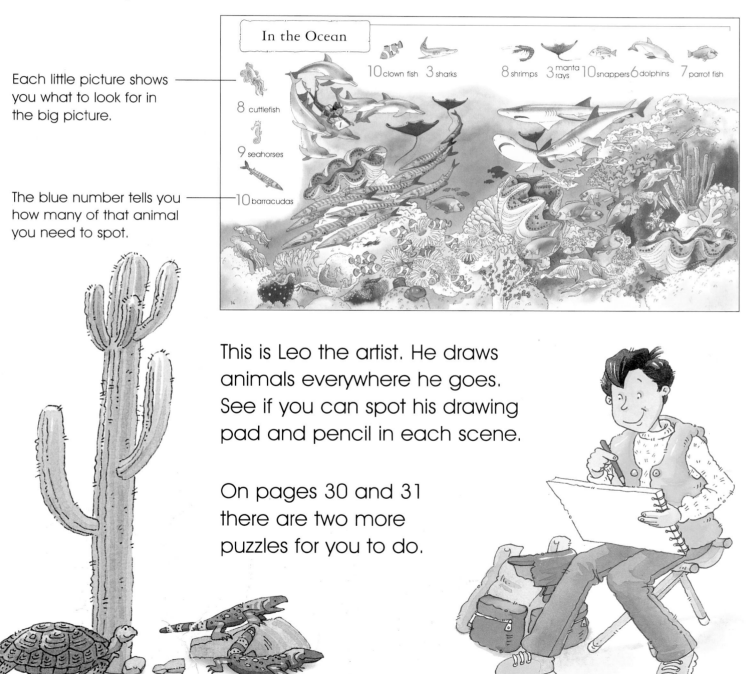

In the Ocean

8 cuttlefish

9 seahorses

10 barracudas

10 clown fish    3 sharks    8 shrimps    3 manta rays    10 snappers    6 dolphins    7 parrot fish

This is Leo the artist. He draws animals everywhere he goes. See if you can spot his drawing pad and pencil in each scene.

On pages 30 and 31 there are two more puzzles for you to do.

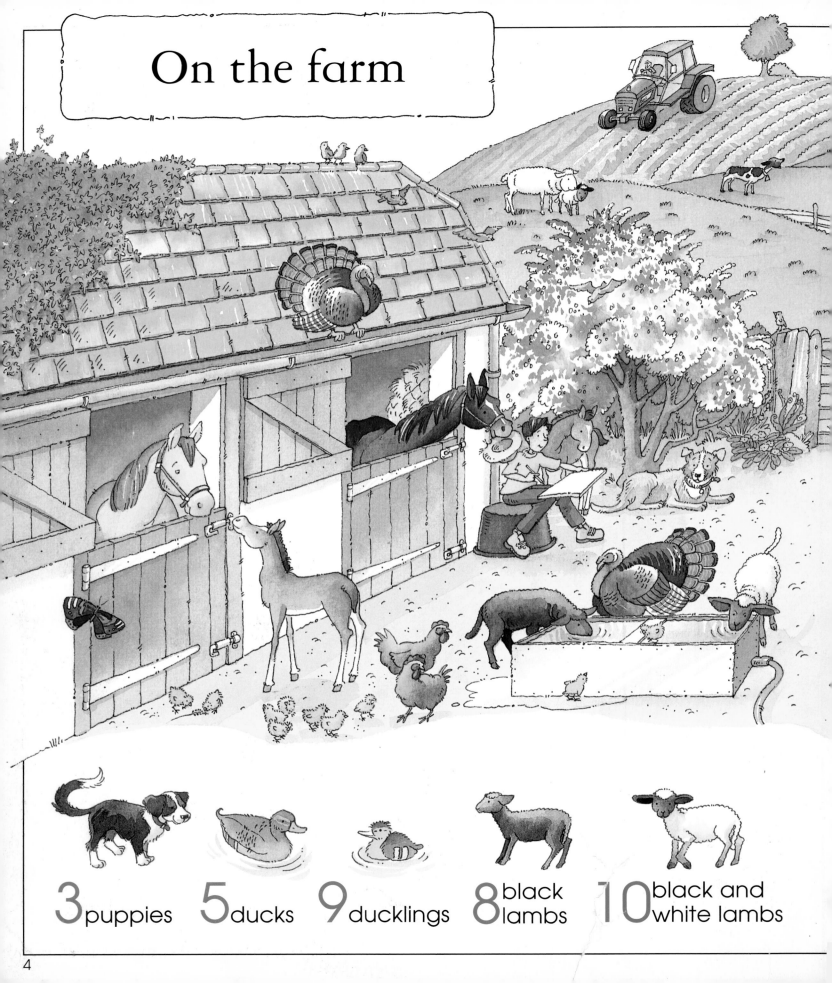

# On the farm

3 puppies  5 ducks  9 ducklings  8 black lambs  10 black and white lambs

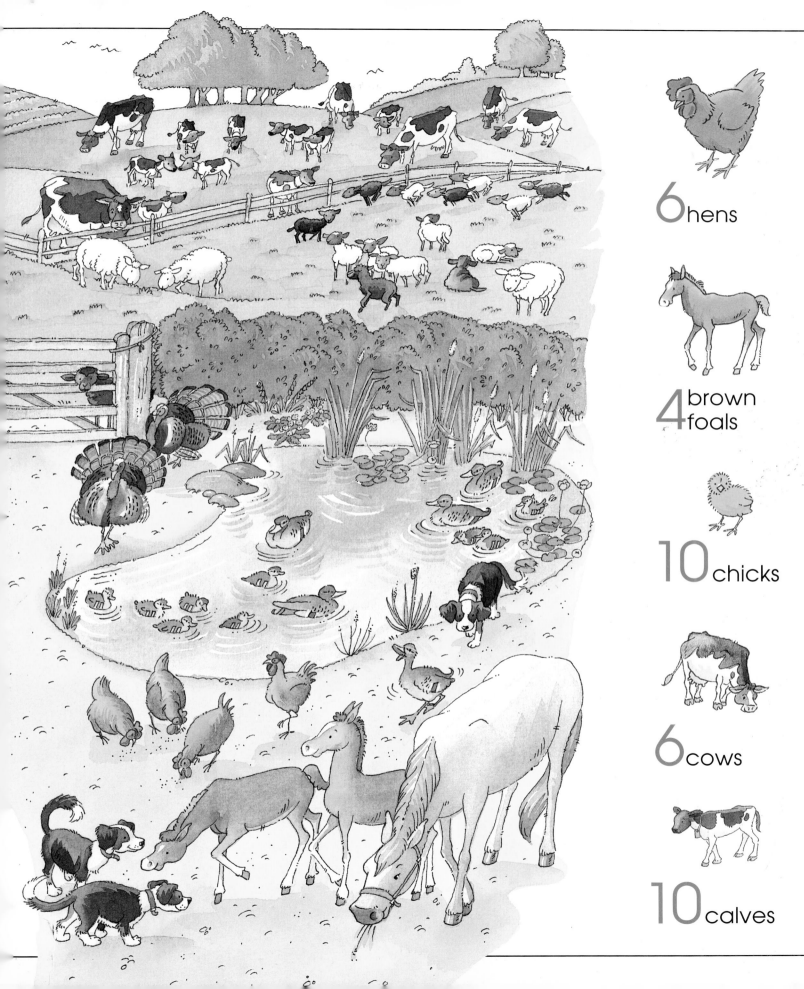

6 hens

4 brown foals

10 chicks

6 cows

10 calves

# On safari

 **10** ostriches

 **4** hippos

 **5** lion cubs

 **4** elephants

 **6** giraffes

6 rhinos  10 zebras  8 vultures  9 warthogs  10 gazelles

# In the desert

10 black ants

4 rattlesnakes

8 scorpions

10 tarantulas

9 painted grasshoppers

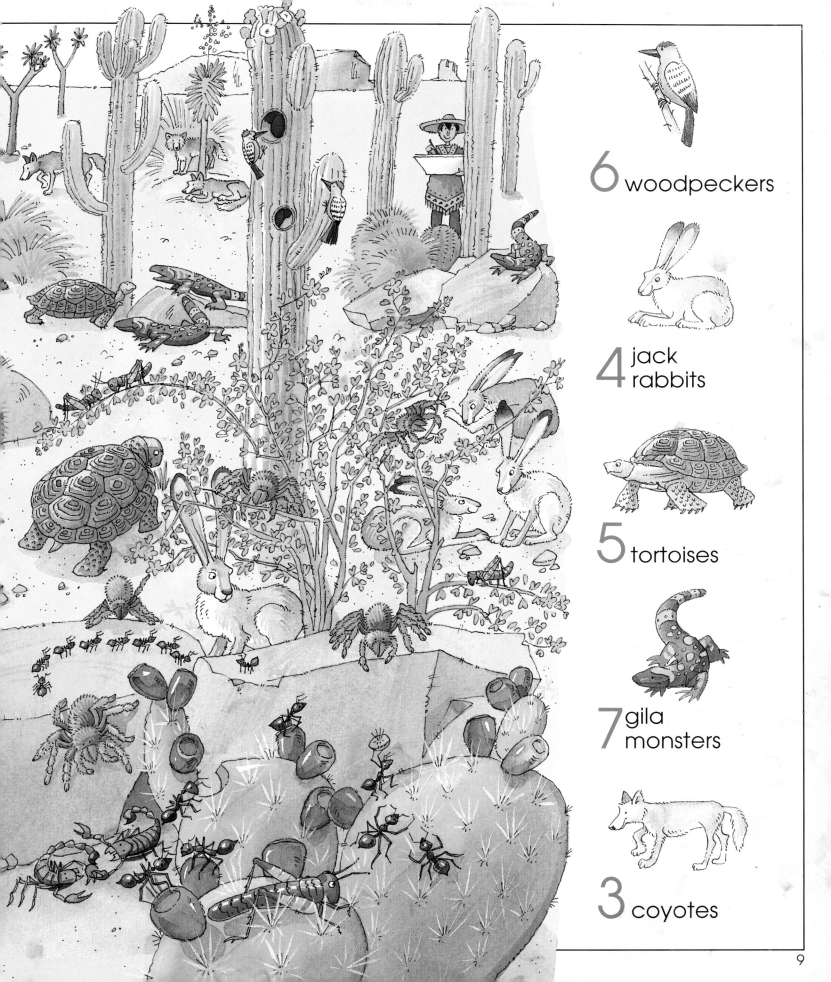

6 woodpeckers

4 jack rabbits

5 tortoises

7 gila monsters

3 coyotes

# In the Arctic

**10** caribou

4 polar bears

 10 seals

 6 snowy owls

 9 lemmings

 1 humpback whale

 6 Arctic foxes

 4 killer whales

 8 baby seals

 5 narwhals

# In the wood

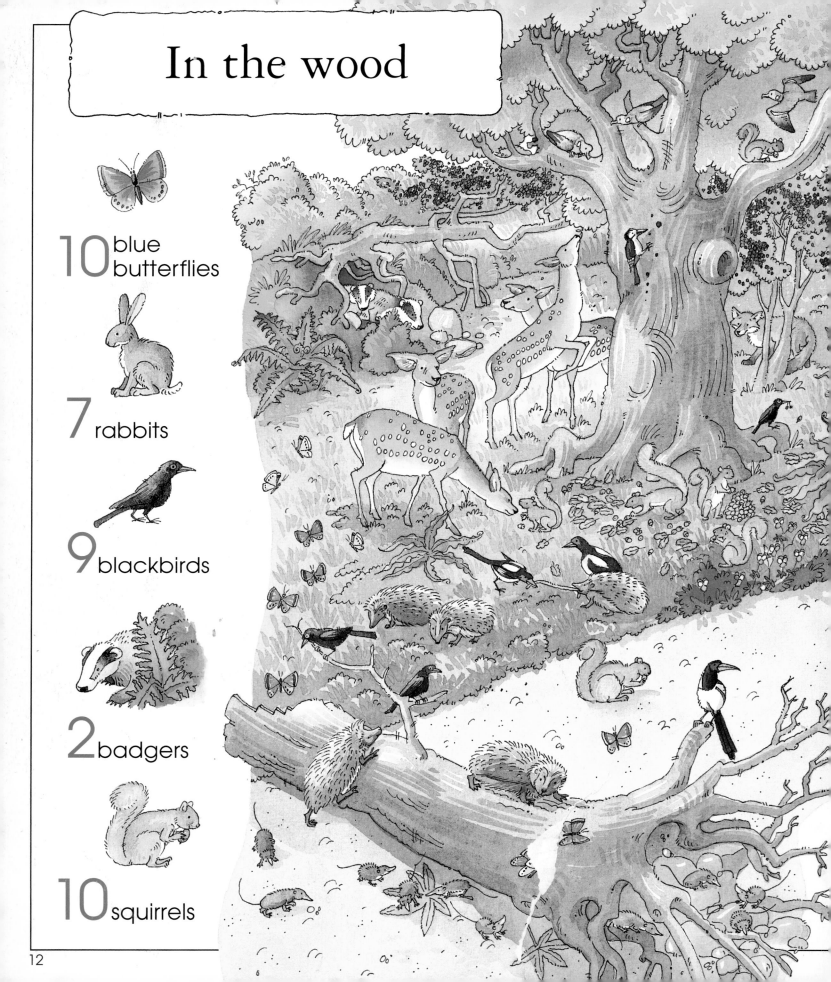

10 blue butterflies

7 rabbits

9 blackbirds

2 badgers

10 squirrels

8 wood pigeons  7 deer  10 hedgehogs  5 foxes  10 shrews

# In the ocean

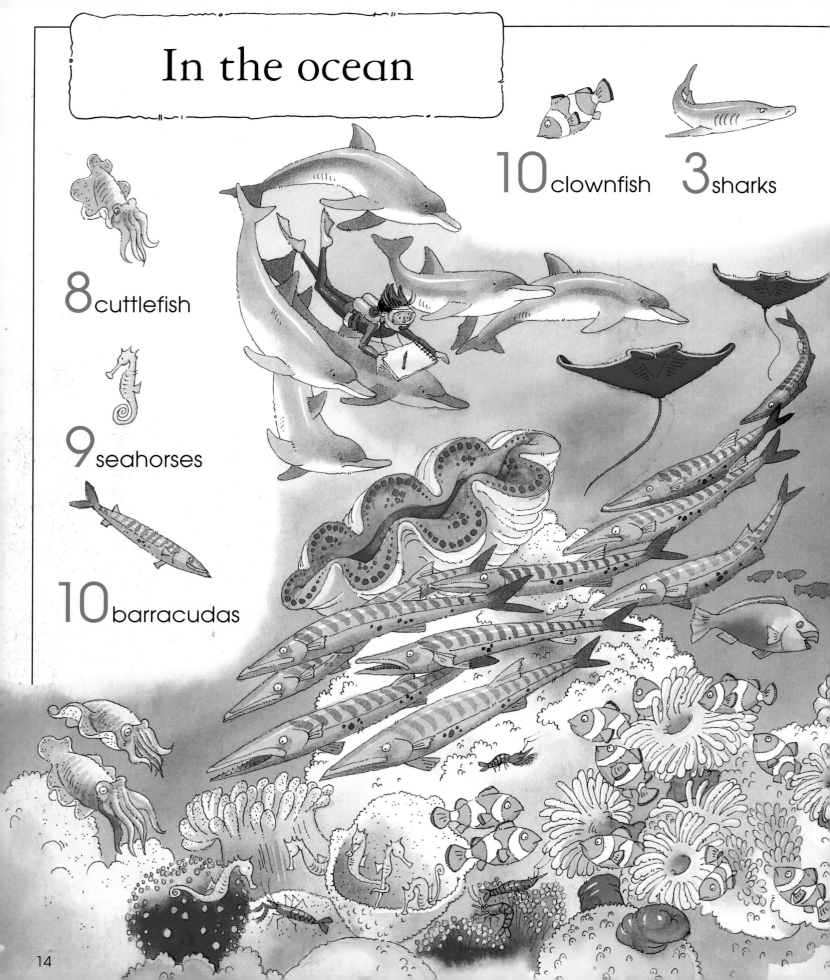

10 clownfish

3 sharks

8 cuttlefish

9 seahorses

10 barracudas

8 shrimps　　3 manta rays　　10 snappers　　6 dolphins　　7 parrotfish

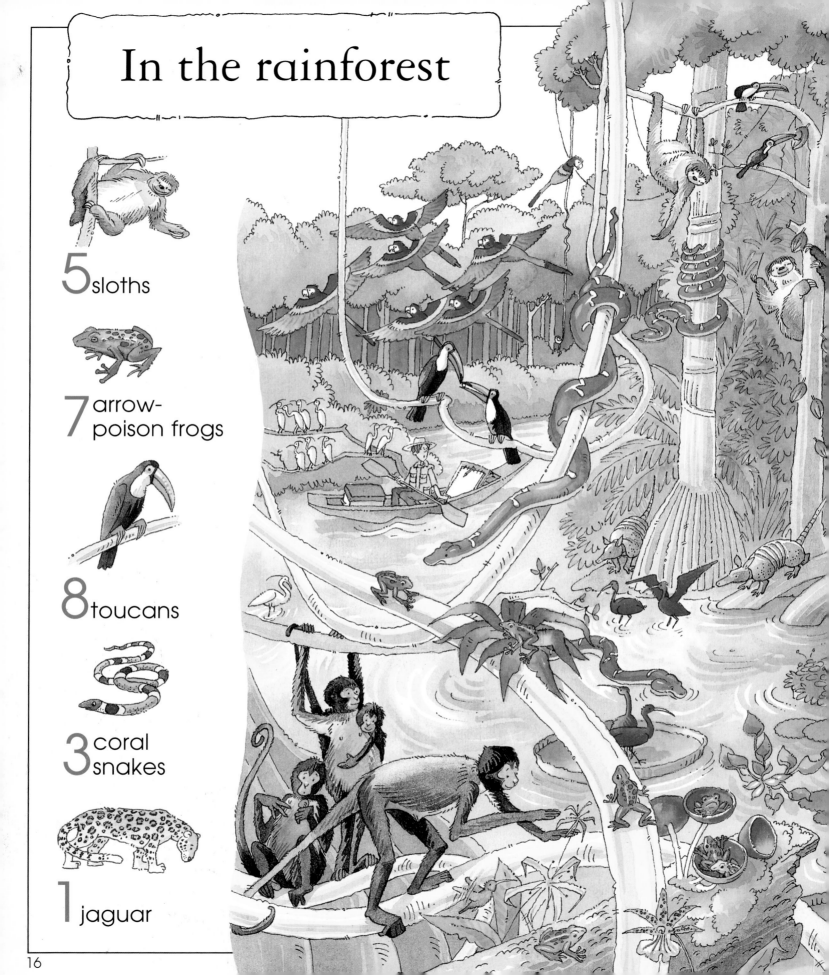

# In the rainforest

**5** sloths

**7** arrow-poison frogs

**8** toucans

**3** coral snakes

**1** jaguar

16

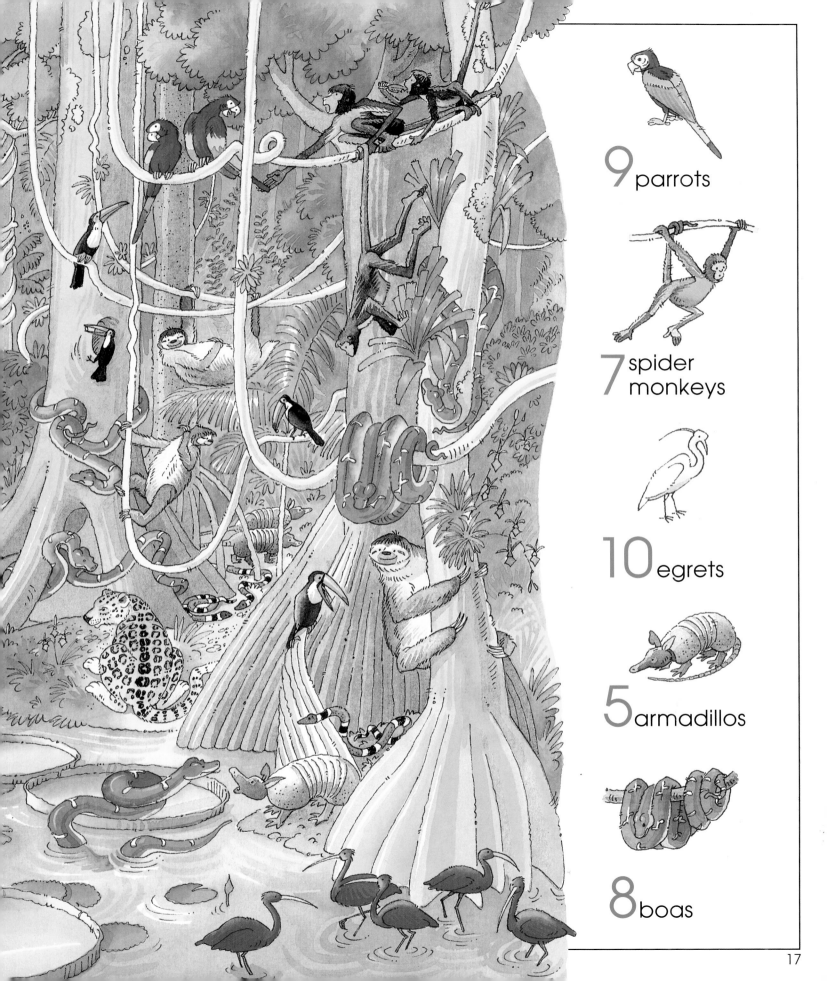

9 parrots

7 spider monkeys

10 egrets

5 armadillos

8 boas

# In the garden

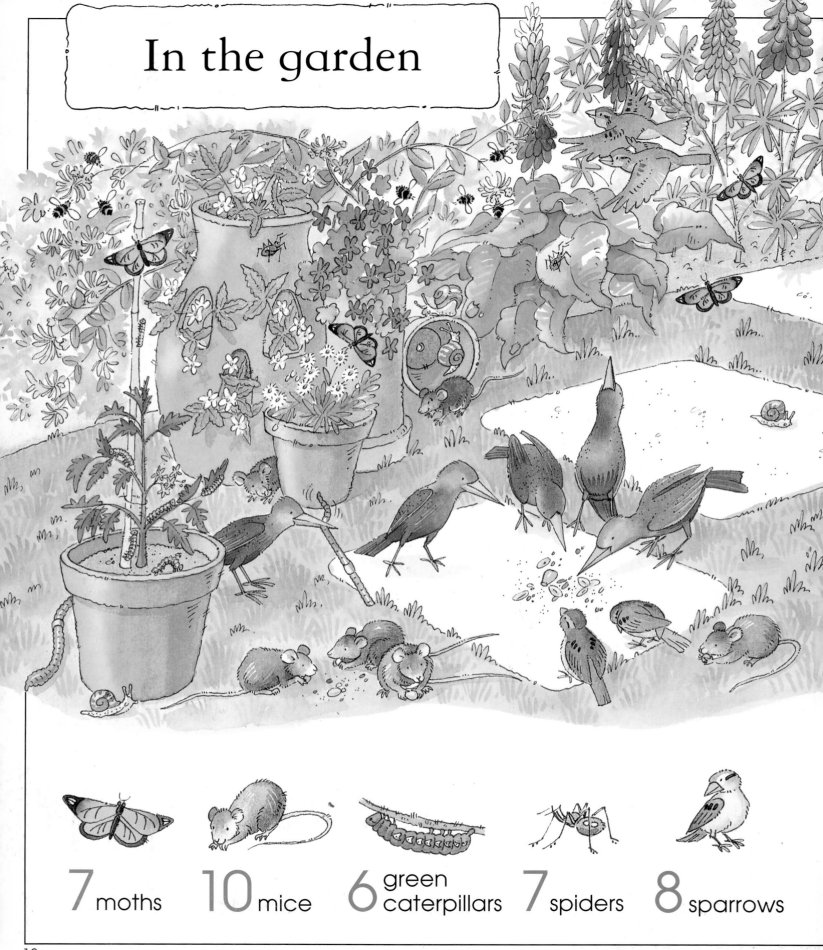

**7** moths  **10** mice  **6** green caterpillars  **7** spiders  **8** sparrows

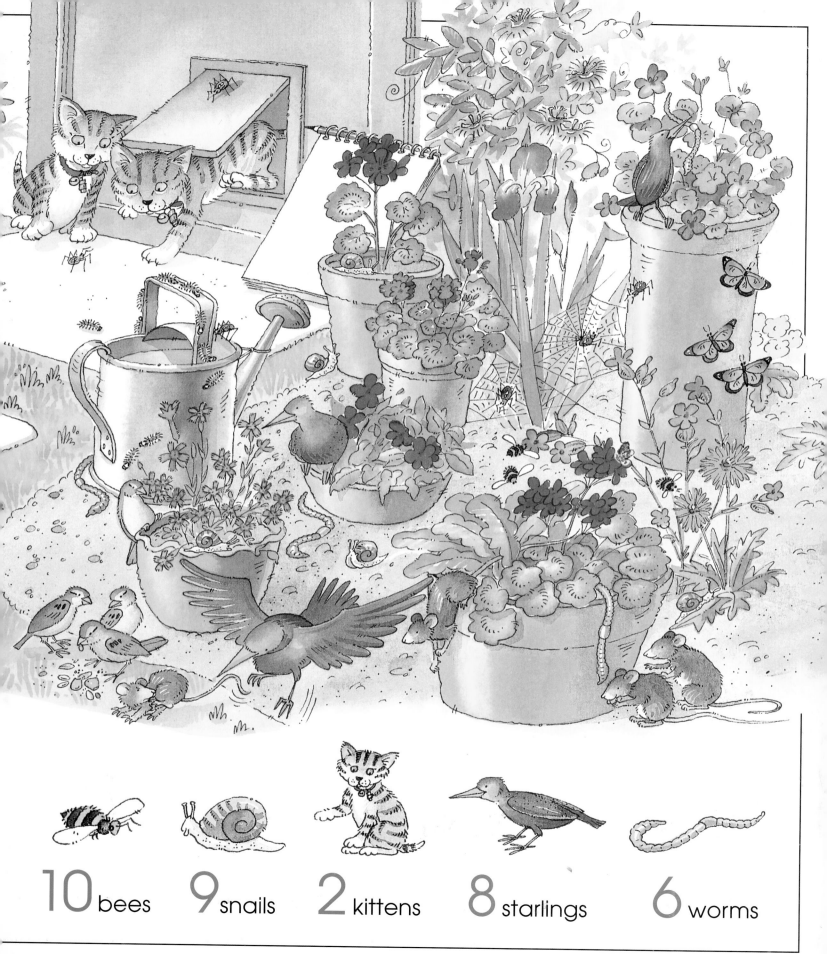

**10** bees  **9** snails  **2** kittens  **8** starlings  **6** worms

# In the outback

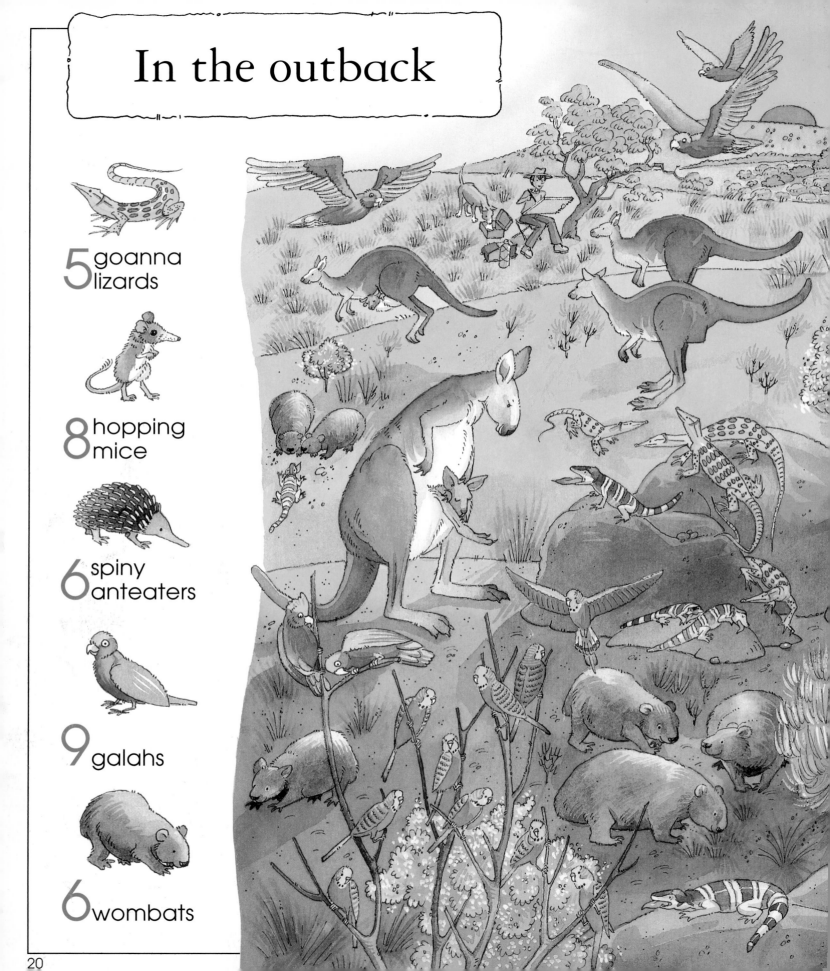

5 goanna lizards

8 hopping mice

6 spiny anteaters

9 galahs

6 wombats

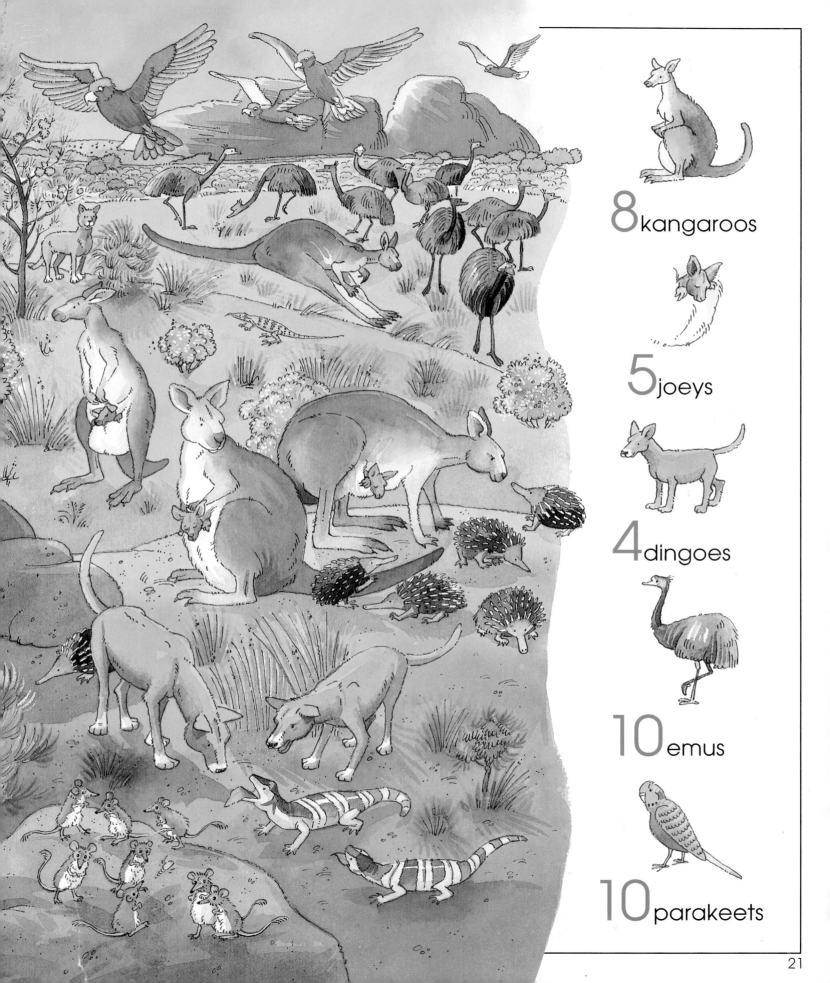

8 kangaroos

5 joeys

4 dingoes

10 emus

10 parakeets

# In the swamp

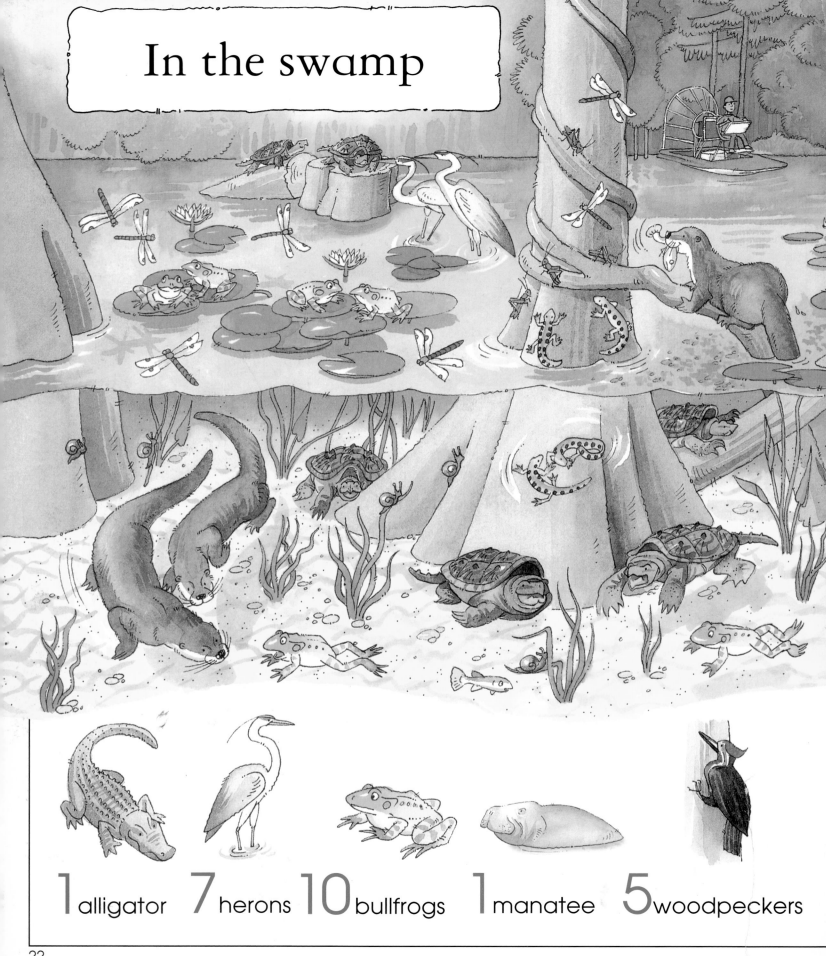

1 alligator 7 herons 10 bullfrogs 1 manatee 5 woodpeckers

8 newts  10 apple snails  10 dragonflies  9 turtles  9 grasshoppers

# In the mountains

**10** butterflies

**9** pikas

**9** mountain goats

**5** eagles

10 geese    7 marmots    3 vultures    1 snow leopard    3 black bears

5 yaks

# By the sea

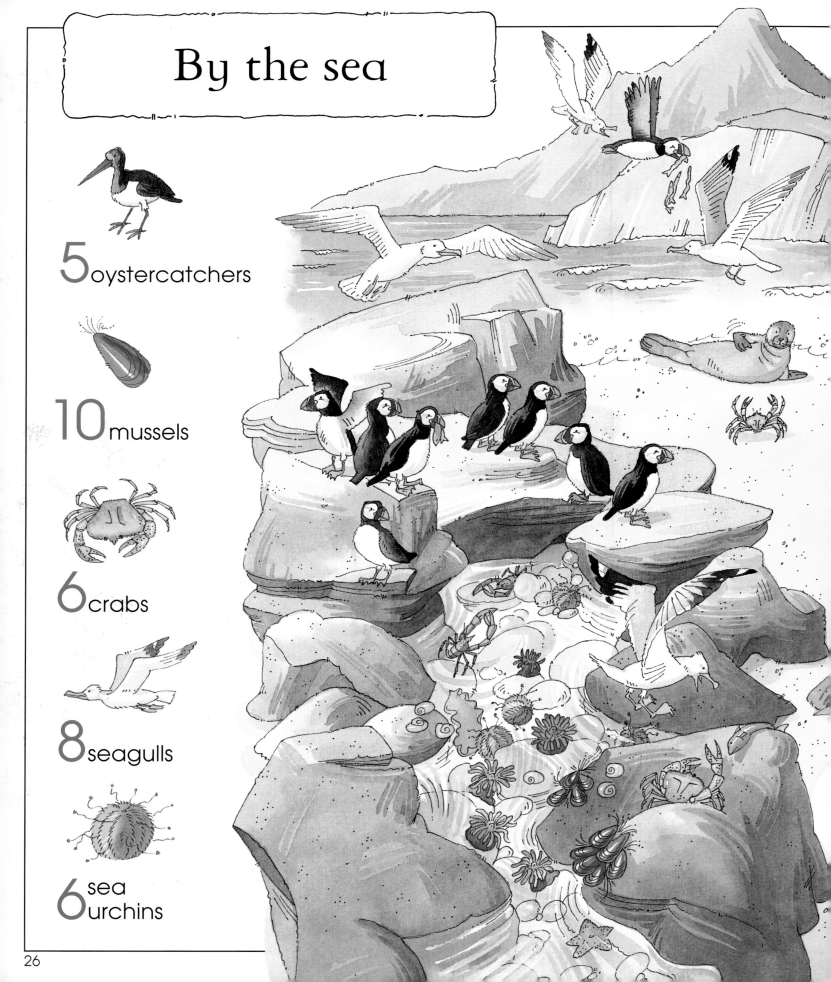

5 oystercatchers

10 mussels

6 crabs

8 seagulls

6 sea urchins

6 seals

 5 squat lobsters

 10 winkles

 10 limpets

 7 sea anemones

# Children's farm

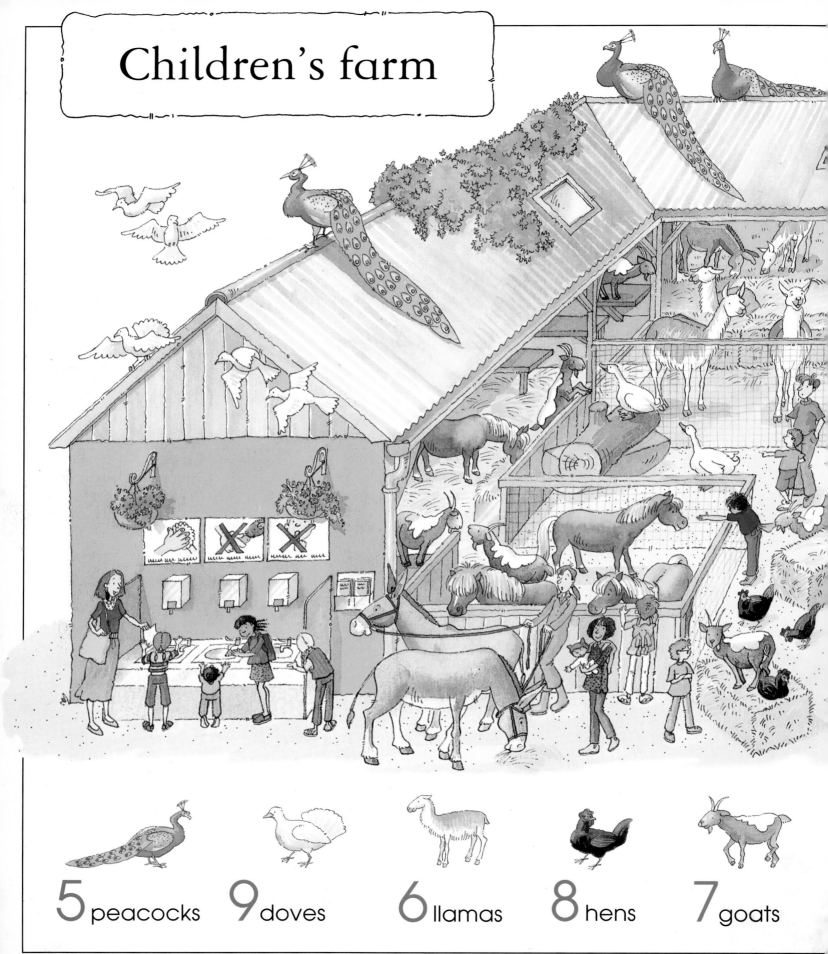

**5** peacocks  **9** doves  **6** llamas  **8** hens  **7** goats

**10** ducks

**5** Shetland ponies

**10** guinea pigs

**3** camels

**10** rabbits

# Leo's pictures

Here are some pictures of animals that Leo drew on his travels. Look back through the book and see if you can find and count them all.

6 otters

9 scarlet ibises

5 magpies

10 wildebeests

7 blue-tongued skinks

9 puffins

10 hairy caterpillars

3 giant clams

9 red ants

10 wallcreepers

4 turkeys

10 walruses

# Close-ups

Have you found all 1001 animals? Here is another game for you to play. These circles show close-ups of animals from earlier in the book. Using the clues, can you name each animal?

Whose stripes are these?

Which animal has just one long tusk?

Who has a blue tongue like this?

Which animal looks like a striped horse?

Whose powerful antlers are these?

Whose tail feathers look like eyes?

Which bird has bright feathers like these?

Whose trumpeting trunk is this?

Which orange striped fish has a funny name?

Which hopping insect has legs like these?

Which fish has green and yellow stripes?

Which animal has a very long neck?

# Answers

Did you find all the animals from Leo's pictures and recognize the animals from the close-ups? Here's where they are.

## Leo's pictures

**6 otters**
In the swamp
(pages 22 and 23)

**9 scarlet ibises**
In the rainforest
(pages 16 and 17)

**5 magpies**
In the wood
(pages 12 and 13)

**10 wildebeests**
On safari
(pages 6 and 7)

**7 blue-tongued skinks**
In the outback
(pages 20 and 21)

**9 puffins**
By the sea
(pages 26 and 27)

**10 hairy caterpillars**
In the garden
(pages 18 and 19)

**3 giant clams**
In the ocean
(pages 14 and 15)

**9 red ants**
In the desert
(pages 8 and 9)

**10 wallcreepers**
In the mountains
(pages 24 and 25)

**4 turkeys**
On the farm
(pages 4 and 5)

**10 walruses**
In the Arctic
(pages 10 and 11)

## Close-ups

 **coral snake**
(pages 16 and 17)

 **narwhal**
(pages 10 and 11)

 **blue-tongued skink**
(pages 20 and 21)

 **zebra**
(pages 6 and 7)

 **caribou**
(pages 10 and 11)

 **peacock**
(pages 28 and 29)

 **parrot**
(pages 16 and 17)

 **elephant**
(pages 6 and 7)

 **clownfish**
(pages 14 and 15)

 **painted grasshopper**
(pages 8 and 9)

 **snapper**
(pages 14 and 15)

 **giraffe**
(pages 6 and 7)

Additional design: Doriana Berkovic Digital manipulation: John Russell
Series editor: Felicity Brooks

### Acknowledgement
The publishers would like to thank the staff at London Zoo's Children's Zoo for their help in the preparation of pages 28 and 29.